Published by Ladybird Books Ltd
27 Wrights Lane London W8 5TZ
A Penguin Company

2 4 6 8 10 9 7 5 3 1

© Jean and Gareth Adamson MMI
The moral rights of the author/illustrator have been asserted

Printed in Italy

Topsy + Tim

Learn opposites

Jean and Gareth Adamson

Ladybird

in and out

Tim pretends his bed is a rabbit's burrow.

He goes in at one end and out at the other.

over and under

Topsy is a rabbit, too. She bunny-hops over her bed and wriggles under it.

on and off

Topsy and Tim get on their bikes and go for a ride. Then they bump into one another and fall off!

laugh and cry

They laugh when they get on their bikes,
but they cry when they fall off.

big and small

Finnegan is a big, friendly dog. Roly Poly is a small, playful puppy. Sometimes they meet in the street.

noisy and quiet

Finnegan quietly wags his tail. Roly Poly barks noisily, "Woof, woof!"

fast and slow

The children are having a race. Some can run very fast, but some are rather slow.

first and last

Kerry came first in the race, Andy came
second and little Stevie Dunton came last.

good and bad

It's bad when Stevie is teased. It's good when someone shouts, "STOP THAT!"

happy and sad

Stevie feels sad, but Topsy and Tim help
pick up his books. Soon he is happy again.

heavy and light

Harriet Hamster is light. The wooden brick is heavy. Topsy and Rai are weighing them on scales.

short and tall

Jamie is short and Josie is tall. Tim is
measuring them on the height chart.

up and down

Tony climbs up the steps of the water chute.

Tim slides down the chute with a big –

SPLASH!

front and back

"I'm swimming on my back," calls Topsy.
"And I'm doing doggy paddle on my front,"
says Kerry.

dangerous and safe

Cars can be dangerous, but Tim and Topsy
feel safe crossing the road with Dad.

stop and go

Dad knows that the red traffic light means
STOP and the green traffic light means GO.

young and old

Grandpa is very old. Tim is very young.

Grandpa and Tim get on well together.

black and white

Granny's hair is white. Topsy's hair is black.
"My hair was black when I was a little girl,"
says Granny.

full and empty

The twins are having a picnic in the garden.

Topsy's cup is empty. Tim's cup is full.

thick and thin

Tim has chosen a great big thick sandwich.

Topsy is eating a thin one.

dirty and clean

It's fun getting dirty in the garden, but it's nice to get clean in the shower.

wet and dry

Tim is wet all over. Topsy is almost dry.

open and closed

Topsy and Tim are in bed. Topsy's eyes are closed, but Tim's are wide open…

awake and asleep

Tim is playing with his toys. He is wide awake while Topsy is fast asleep.